THE
HAUNTED COAST

Staithes

Copyright © 2002
The Cædmon Storytellers
Published by East Coast Books
Printed by Baker Printers Ltd – Whitby

REMEMBER THEE!
AY, THOU POOR GHOST,
WHILE MEMORY HOLDS A SEAT
IN THIS DISTRACTED GLOBE.

HAMLET

CONTENTS

PIERS GAVESTON OF SCARBOROUGH

OCCASIONALLY, *if they are lucky*, people walking high above the sea by the walls of Scarborough Castle see the headless spirit of Piers Gaveston rushing towards them, ghostly blood still gushing from the severed arteries in its neck. And following the body, comes the head - pulling itself along the ground by its teeth, a wild and vicious look in its eyes.

I say *lucky*, not because many people like to see such sights, but because those who fail to notice this ghost approaching them are pushed violently over the cliff's edge, falling a hundred yards or so to a gruesome, mangled death on the rocks below.

Piers Gaveston was the favourite of King Edward the Second. Edward was a peaceful man unable to measure up to his father's warlike reputation. Eventually, in 1327, he was murdered by his noblemen in a most barbarous manner.

His chief fault was that HE LOVED the company of HIS FRIEND Piers Gaveston above anyone, even that of his wife, Queen Isabella, who was said to be the most beautiful woman in Europe. Edward would not listen to any of his barons or knights; it was Piers Gaveston alone who had his ear. As if this was not bad enough, Gaveston was a Gascon - a French Man! Worse even than this, was Gaveston's attitude to the barons. He laughed at them, FLAUNTED his influence over the king, and gave them insulting nicknames. The earl of Warwick, for instance, he called the 'BLACK DOG-OF ARDEN' because he was dark and hairy, while the Earl of Lancaster he named the 'PLAY ACTOR' due to his peculiar voice.

After so many slights and insults at Gaveston's hands, the

nobles of the kingdom got together and threatened rebellion, forcing Edward to send his favourite abroad. But the King could not bear to be without his friend, and after a few months summoned the nobles of England, and begged them to let Gaveston return, making them promises that he would control his friend's behaviour in the future.

The noblemen reluctantly agreed, but soon Gaveston was behaving as badly as before, and the king did nothing to stop him. The Nobles, outraged, rose in revolt, and the king, fearing for his friend's safety, sent him to SCARBOROUGH CASTLE, which was said to be the STRONGEST FORTRESS IN ENGLAND. The castle was besieged, and although the Barons failed to break down the walls in a month's bombardment, they did prevent any supplies from being delivered. Finally, weak with hunger, Gaveston surrendered the castle and its garrison on the condition that he be taken to London and delivered safely to the king.

A few miles north of Oxford, the convoy which was taking Piers to London suddenly halted, and from his hiding place appeared the Earl of Warwick - The Black Dog of Arden. PIERS HAD BEEN TRICKED. He was dragged away, not to London, but to Warwick Castle, where several of the other nobles whom he had insulted were waiting.

The Earl of Warwick took down a great war axe from the wall and, touching the blade significantly, said to his prisoner:

"NOW YOU SHALL FEEL THE TEETH OF THIS BLACK DOG?"

Gaveston was dragged from the castle, screaming and crying for mercy. He was hauled up a local landmark known as BLACKLOW HILL and there beheaded by the Earl himself.

It has always been something of a mystery as to why Gaveston's ghost should choose to haunt Scarborough Castle, shoving innocent holiday makers to their deaths. After all, the town suffered siege, bombardment and starvation to protect him. Why did he not haunt the site of his betrayal at Oxford or death at Warwick? One possible explanation is that neither Warwick nor Oxford could afford Gaveston the fine sea views, the healthy airs, or the multitude of tourist attractions for which the Old Town of Scarborough is now rightly famous!

BOGIES, GHOSTS, HOBS, HAGS *AND* FAIRIES

THE COAST between Sandsend and Staithes is heavily haunted by a variety of interesting apparitions. Sandsend was once the abode of the 'Sandsend Bogey'. It was said to live in the cupboard of a local cottage and would go out to sea with the fishermen, its presence guaranteeing them a good catch. It was finally exorcised by the Lythe priest when it took to frightening the local children.

Mulgrave Woods below Lythe was once said to be haunted by "JEANIE OF BIGGERDALE", a witch or sprite who disliked visitors to her domain. Traditionally people were said to call her name then run away before she could catch them, giving rise to the old rhyme:

BIGGERDALE JEANIE WHERE IS THOO?
AH'S NOBBUT TYING MY LEFT FOOT SHOO!
BIDE! AN AH'LL BE WI THEE-NOO!

One particular tale of Jeanie, who pursued a local farmer and his horse, finally ripping the animal in two as it leapt over a stream to safety, is said to have inspired Robert Burns' "Tam-o-shanter", although the horse in his story loses only its tail. Local children today, however, know nothing about Jeanie, and instead fear the "Pad Pad". This beast, half human, half goat, haunts a tunnel beneath the old Mulgrave Castle, and acts in much the same as Jeanie is said to have done in her prime.

Towards Runswick Bay there was once a cave known as Hob-hole. Hob-hole was said to be the home of a goblin who had the power of curing little children afflicted with whooping cough. If a child was suffering from that disease, one of its parents would carry it to the cave and with a loud voice shout: "HOB-HOLE HOB! MY BAIRN'S GOT KINK-COUGH; TAK'T OFF! TAK'T OFF." And sure enough, within a month the child was cured. Or Dead!

A little inland from Runswick itself is Claymore Well, from which the noises of fairies beating their washing with "bittles" occasionally emerges. The well is best avoided, for fairies in this part of the world have a somewhat sinister reputation, and occasionally emerge to abduct people who are passing by.

The Staithes area is well stocked with ghosts of folk who had fatal accidents. In 1846 a fisherman known as James Harrison fell six hundred feet from the Boulby Cliffs. His ghost was seen so frequently by his relatives, even having conversations with them, that eventually a priest was called to try to exorcise the spirit, but with only partial success. Though his ghost is still seen occasionally at Boulby, it would be unwise to attempt to engage him in close conversation, for the part of the cliff on which Harrison's spirit walks fell many years ago, and he floats in mid-air 20 feet or so out over the sea.

Another ghost still appears in the village, usually in spring, floating across the little bridge which links Staithes and Cowbar. Her gory end was recorded by George Young, the historian in 1817:

"The most singular accident that ever happened on the coast occurred about 15 years ago, under the high cliffs a little to the west of Staithes, while two little girls of of the name Grundy, belonging to Staithes, were sitting on the scar, or rocky beach, with their backs to the cliff, a splinter, which by striking a ledge had acquired a rotary motion, fell from the cliff, and hitting one of the girls on the hinder part of the neck, severed her head from her body in a moment, and the head rolled to a considerable distance along the scar."

EBENEEZER CREAKE
OF FILEY

"Less than twenty years ago Filey was a simple fishing village, now it is a
fashionable watering town, bidding fair, in the course of a few years, to
claim a place in the first rank of watering places".
A General History and Description of the County of York. 1856.

FIRST IMPRESSIONS of Filey tend to be of Victorian
splendour, the majestic crescent, the manicured flower-beds, the
fine and well ordered gardens. Every year the council holds a
festival celebrating its Victorian heritage, with brass bands, barrel
organs, Punch & Judy shows and the like. But Filey existed long
before the splendid crescent was built. For many centuries a tiny
fishing village had nestled by the shore, virtually isolated from
the rest of the world. Few outsiders visited the place, and if they
did, they were greeted with suspicion if they were lucky, a hail of
stones and a volley of abuse if they were not. The people had such
a reputation for ungodliness that meetings were held in
Bridlington to pray for the safe return of the local vicar when he
made the perilous journey to preach there. Eventually the coming
of the railways eroded the isolation of Filey folk, the building of
the crescent altered their employment, and Methodism turned
them into the honest God-fearing people that they are today.

Not all succumbed easily to the modern world, however.
EBENEEZER CREAKE was a rough old fisherman and
smuggler. In his time he had fought the revenue men with pistol
and cutlass. A great scar stretched from his right eye to his chin,
gained from battling with another gang of smugglers. His right
arm was missing - ripped off by chainshot when he served his

country in the ROYAL NAVY.

Ebeneezer had been pressed into the navy, and the time spent in the service of His Majesty was unhappy. Ebeneezer was an independently minded man who did not like to take orders. However, the cruel punishments handed out by the navy soon convinced him of the wisdom of obedience to his officers. While the service was hard, and the conditions brutal, the greatest suffering inflicted on Ebeneezer was by the CAPTAIN'S BAND. The Captain, being a cultured man, kept musicians for his own entertainment and, so he said, the morale of the crew. The band did little for Ebeneezer's morale, however. They would play 'The Roast Beef of Old England' before dinner, and Ebeneezer would be fed not roast beef but pickled cart horse. Before battle the band stood on the quarter deck and played 'Come Cheer up My Lads 'tis to Glory We Steer' as they steered towards the flaming mouths of their enemies' cannons. And on a Sunday, the whole crew were assembled and made to sing hymns for an hour. As a result Ebeneezer developed a dislike to brass bands which was to stay with him beyond his grave.

Discharged from service after losing an arm, Ebeneezer went back to his fishing, relieved to turn his back on the strange ways of the outside world. However, he saw with dismay that the outside world was creeping into Filey, bringing holiday makers, trains, donkey rides and religion. Often, while working on the beach, mending his nets or painting his boat, Ebeneezer would look up the hill and glower in disgust at the sight of the growing new town.

To add insult to injury, the newly formed council employed a small BRASS BAND who wore bottle green military-style coats and played for six hours a day every day during the season. In calm weather the sound of this brass band would waft down the hill and could be heard if you LISTENED CAREFULLY. Strangely enough, Old Ebeneezer listened more carefully than any one else. He would complain to his neighbours about the noise "THEM FOREIGNERS" were making. And at first his neighbours agreed with him whole heartedly. Gradually though, as they began to benefit from the presence of "them foreigners", they became less certain. Now that their children began to work in the hotels, their husbands to take out fishing parties, they began to avoid old Ebeneezer and his "mad rantings".

Now, you might have expected that Ebeneezer would keep away from this hated new town, but this was not the case. In the same way as when we chip a tooth, we cannot stop ourselves from constantly exploring the damage with our tongue, so Ebeneezer was constantly drawn up the hill to view the crescent, the fancy ladies with their parasols, and to hear the brass band which he hated so much. He would walk around the crescent, a bewildered look on his face, before stopping some unsuspecting visitor or other and saying reproachfully: "This was all fields, this was." And he was always surprised that their reply was usually along the lines of: "Yes, isn't progress wonderful."

He spent so much time walking in the new town that he became known as something of a character and the ladies would greet him with a "Good morning captain." Legends grew of how he lost his arm. Some said it was a shark that bit it off, some that he ate it himself when shipwrecked on the coast of Scotland. Others claimed that he was the last surviving crew member of HMS Serapis and had lost his arm fighting that notorious pirate John Paul Jones off Flamborough Head.

Eventually old Ebeneezer, the last of the "Old Filey" folk passed away. He was buried in the parish church yard, his feet pointing to the sea, but his head towards the new town.

Occasionally, on moonlit nights, holiday makers staying on Filey's fine Victorian Crescent, while looking out to sea or at the moon, notice from the corner of their eye the ghosts of VICTORIAN VISITORS walking around the crescent just as they had in life. Astonished, they look down to get a better view, but even as they do, these figures fade away, leaving only a few fragmented images in the mind of the beholder - perhaps a gentleman raising his hat to a lady, maybe a couple of well dressed children chasing hoops. But sometimes amongst these smiling ghosts there is seen another figure, in sharp contrast to them. A ghost almost amongst these happy ghosts. For in death, as in life, Ebeneezer wanders the Crescent, one sleeve of his old gansey flapping in the breeze, a miserable look on his pale, ghostly face, condemned to walk forever in death amongst that which he most despised in life.

THE HEADLESS FARMER
OF ROBIN HOOD'S BAY

IT IS SURPRISING to know that the farming folk of Yorkshire were once famously TIGHT-FISTED, rather than the open handed and generous folk that they are today.

In the nineteenth century all of the farmers around Robin Hood's Bay were what we might call 'frugal'. But there was one family amongst these 'TIGHT-NEEVED' folk who were regarded even by them as misers: the MARSHALLS. The Marshalls would never throw something away if it could be patched up or mended. They would go to ridiculous lengths to save a penny. They would spend hours hammering old nails flat to reuse them even though they always bent again, making their barns and fences crooked. Their farming tools were worked for years until they were at the point of collapse, and even then they would attempt to borrow a tool from their neighbours rather than buy one new.

Every morning the family ate porridge, and it there was any left over, it did not go to waste, for old Mrs. Marshall would pour the porridge into a drawer, leave it to cool and go hard, then give slices of it to her children, telling them it was cake.

Old 'Bert' Marshall was the pride of this cheese-paring crop, notorious for miles around for his false teeth. At a neighbour's funeral, he had noticed that the deceased had a set of false teeth and, reasoning that the dead man could have no further use for them, in a quiet moment, plucked them from the corpse's mouth. Later that day, as his own teeth were in poor condition, he had his son pull out the blackened stumps with an old pair of rusty pliers and began to wear the false ones in their place.

Bert had an old and bony mare which he used to ride around on. Being so very old and so very bony, the animal had great difficulty in getting up the steep hills around Robin Hood's Bay. But Bert was reluctant to pay good money for a new horse, and he would either dismount and walk on the steepest slopes, or avoid them altogether by going a longer way round. One useful route he occasionally took was along what was then the new Whitby-Scarborough railway line.

While Bert was generally loath to spend his money on unnecessary luxuries, one thing he did not stint himself on was beer. This he consumed copiously on a Friday night, riding five miles on his boney old mare to the WINDMILL INN at Stainsacre, where the beer was a farthing cheaper than in his local pub. He would pull out his teeth the better to savour his beer for they were, he admitted, a little uncomfortable, but would pop them back in if he had to speak to anyone.

IT WAS A DARK AND STORMY NIGHT when Old Bert made his way home along the railway line after an evening of drinking. Exactly how the accident happened nobody knows. Perhaps an overhanging branch caught his head and knocked him out. Or maybe his false teeth slipped out, and Bert, snatching for them as they fell, toppled from his mare. But however it happened, Bert tumbled from his horse and landed across the railway line. Nor do we know whether the fall killed him outright, or if he was lying unconscious when the first train to come along in the morning severed his head. The train driver, rather shaken, and guessing that nothing could be done for Old Bert, continued on to the next station before raising the alarm.

Hours later, when the police came to recover Old Bert's body, they were unable to find his head, and what became of it was never known. Some people, though, were of the opinion that a fox had carried it off to his den for breakfast.

Bert's family spent several days searching for the old man's head, for in those days it was felt important to bury all of the parts of a body together in the grave so that they would all be ready to come out again on the day of judgment. But more importantly for the Marshall family was the dread that the head would turn up after the funeral and put them to the extra expense of a second burial. Eventually Bert was interred without his head in a short and (cheaper) coffin - along with his teeth, which the undertaker had found clenched firmly in the corpse's fist.

The spirit of Old Bert does not lie easy in its grave. Perhaps in the afterlife it faced having to purchase a new and expensive head. On moonless nights Old Bert's ghost is still seen on the railway line, searching for its missing part.

It is a terrifying sight too: a headless ghost blundering sightlessly into bushes, tripping over stones or stumbling into ditches, one arm stretched out graspingly in front. And in other are the GHOSTLY FALSE TEETH, glowing weirdly in the darkness. Occasionally the ghost pauses and clacks the teeth like maraccas, the ghostly sound carrying through the air, silencing the owls and the scurrying creatures of the night. Vainly it waits, hoping for some response from the missing head, then plunges on in its eternal, hopeless quest.

Robin Hood's Bay
From the South

THE BOUNCING-BALL OF RUNSWICK BAY

RUNSWICK BAY is a pretty little village, sadly almost deserted now, for the natives or "Nagars" have gradually dispersed during the last fifty years, moving away for work or up to the top of the hill where the houses are cheaper. The cottages of the old village down by the sea are now almost exclusively holiday homes, and valuable too - with the exception of one, which comes onto the market every few years, and is sold at a remarkably low price.

Two hundred years ago things were very different. Runswick was then a thriving fishing village, tourism unheard of. One of the better known characters of the village was "CROOK BACK TOM", the carpenter. Tom's father had been the village carpenter in his time, and had apprenticed his son at a very early age. It was said that Tom had a crooked back from carrying great BAULKS of timber from the tender age of three. Tom made furniture, repaired fishing boats, and as a sideline acted as the village undertaker, doing everything from digging the hole to making the coffin.

Tom worked hard and was fond of his drink. And this was rather unfortunate, for his large and overbearing wife was opposed to the consumption of alcohol as a matter of principle, and would confiscate any money Tom made to prevent him from tippling. Tom was not to be deprived of his chief pleasure so easily, however, and he took to doing "LITTLE JOBS" for people in exchange for "a few pints", which he supped in the old Royal Hotel. Sad to say, the jobs which Tom did for beer proved to be very much cheaper to his clients than those which paid cash.

Indeed, he undercut himself so badly that soon no-one employed him on a cash basis at all, and he became a drunken bankrupt. As a result, Tom woke one morning with a dreadful headache and empty pockets. Worse still, he found that his wife had run away, leaving behind their only child, a little daughter called Kate.

Tom desperately tried to straighten out his affairs but people, having enjoyed his services at very low prices, were reluctant to pay the market rate. Soon the village was full of wobbling chairs, creaking doors and leaky boats. Indeed the only time he could be guaranteed an income was when someone died, and even then the relatives would frequently break off in the midst of their mourning to complain bitterly about Tom's heartless "profiteering".

While Kate was a shy and timid child - unlike her mother - she shared her dislike of Tom's drinking. This was not out of principal, but because he terrified her when he was intoxicated, swaying around the room when he came home, singing badly, or crying over his misfortunes.

One fateful afternoon, Tom was penniless and desperate for work. Having been sober for over a week, he agreed to do some repairs on an old, leaky boat in return for some beer. This upset his daughter somewhat, for they had been living on porridge and water for several days. Little Kate began to cry. Tom, sensing a reproach in her tears, called her a naughty girl, and decided to punish her by locking her in a little cupboard by the stairs before setting out to work. As a concession, he let her take with her into the cubby-hole A LITTLE RUBBER BALL which was her favourite toy.

In days past, the men of the North East coast had a deserved reputation as hardy sailors, and in time of war the Royal Navy would cruise the waters and would press fishermen into their service. And so it was that Tom, working in the boat, was forced into the navy by a press gang who had sneakily landed several miles up the coast, skirted round the back of the village, and rushed down the steep bank to take the unsuspecting fishermen in the rear.

In spite of his crooked back and the fact that he had never before been to sea, Tom proved to be a good catch for the navy. Firstly, his carpentry skills were sorely needed in those days of wooden boats, and secondly, under the strict discipline of the navy, Tom blossomed, and was promoted many times. Even his back improved from the constant exercise of ducking beneath the low beams between the decks, and climbing up the rigging.

So it was that at the conclusion of the war, when Tom was honourably discharged from the navy with enough prize money to keep him for life, he would hardly have been recognised as the shrunken drunkard who had been pressed five years before. He set off from Hartlepool, a jaunty spring in his step, a bright parrot on his shoulder, and his shiny tools in a smart painted box under his strong, suntanned arm. It was well after dark when he reached Runswick Bay. He made his way down the bank and came to his little cottage. There, expecting things to be just how he had left them, he was surprised to find the door unlocked, swinging to and fro in the night breeze. He entered and felt sand beneath his feet, cobwebs brushing his face. Little Kate, he thought must have gone to live with one of his neighbours when he had been taken, but he was surprised that she had not looked after the empty house. Deciding it was rather late to be knocking his neighbours up, Tom lay down to sleep on a chair, covering himself with his coat. But a gentle but **PERSISTENT NOISE** came tap-tap-tapping from up the stairs. Tom thought it was an open window moving in the wind, but on going to investigate, found them all secure.

The next morning Tom went in search of his daughter, knocking at the nearest door. The housewife who opened it did not at first recognise the smart sailor who stood before her, but turned pale when she did. She beckoned him in and made him sit down and drink a strong cup of tea before she told him of the awful fate which befell his daughter.

FIVE YEARS BEFORE, when Tom and several other local men had been impressed, the village had gone into a state of mourning. It was almost a week before anyone noticed that Kate had also disappeared. Eventually a search of the cottage was made, and the little girl was found, still locked in the cupboard. In her hand, clutched tightly, was her little rubber ball. But she was dead, of course.

No one blamed Tom for locking his daughter in the cupboard, for in those hard days, such punishments and worse were the fashion, it being said "SPARE THE ROD, SPOIL THE CHILD". They tried to comfort him, saying that she probably died of fright when he closed the door and so did not suffer long, though they knew that this was untrue: for the wall and floor of the cupboard was marked with hundreds of black dots where the girl had bounced her little ball in the darkness. Indeed, it had been the talk of the village as to why she had stayed in the cupboard, for the door was a flimsy one which she could easily have broken down if she had really wanted.

That night Tom stayed in his house for the last time, and again he was disturbed by a persistent banging noise. This time he carefully followed the sound, and found to his horror that it came from the very cupboard in which Kate had perished. And now he recognised the noise, the tap-tap-tapping; it was the sound of a rubber ball being bounced over and over again against the wall. The next morning, Tom fled the village never to return.

The cottage in Runswick Bay is still haunted by the ghost of Little Kate. The incessant noise of the ghostly ball tap-tap-tapping on certain nights drives out every owner within a year. And legend states that her spirit will never leave the little cupboard until the ghost of her father returns to let her out.

JENNY GALLOWS
OF FLAMBOROUGH

THE LITTLE VILLAGE of Flamborough was the birthplace of Henry Freeman, sole survivor of the great 1861 Whitby life boat disaster. It is also the haunt of a ghost or sprite know as Jenny Gallows. Flamborough is a secluded spot. A few tourists may stop for a pot of tea after visiting one of the picturesque beaches on the nearby coast, but generally, it's a quiet place. And that is how Jenny Gallows likes it.

Jenny Gallows haunts the village, lying peacefuly in coalsheds, concealing herself in long grass or lurking in dark alleyways.

Jenny is only seen by children. NOISY CHILDREN. Noisy children who disturb her in the quiet contemplation of her surroundings.

A traditional scenario will have a group of noisy boys running down a street kicking a tin can in front of them, laughing, shouting, only to fall silent, quaking with fear, as they hear the dreaded words:

AH'LL PUT ON MI BONNET
AN TEE ON MI SHOE
IF THOO'S NOT OFF
. . . . AH BE AFTER THOO

as Jenny prepares herself for pursuit.

Now the children run, helter-skelter, but in perfect silence, seeking safety, knowing they must get away.

How Jenny came to haunt Flamborough is not known, nor does anyone appear to know what would happen if she actually caught a child who did not run away fast enough.

It is also interesting to note that no children living in Flamborough today have ever seen or heard Jenny. But they all know about her. For if ever they are noisy, jumping on their beds and pillow-fighting instead of sleeping, then their parents, who have, of course, been chased by Jenny in their youth, warn them to get into bed and be quiet or "JENNY GALLOWS WILL COME AND GET YOU". And the children, as silent as Jenny Gallows herself could desire, slip obediently into their beds and so to sleep.

The lighthouse, Flamborough Head

THE HAUNTED COAST

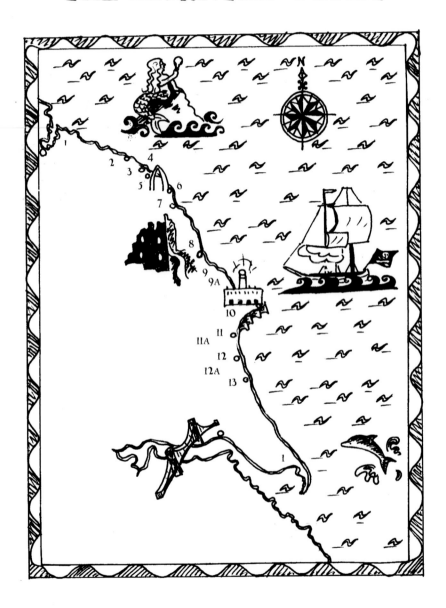

SITES OF GHOSTS IN THIS BOOK... AND A FEW WHICH WE COULDN'T FIT INTO *THIS* LITTLE VOLUME

THE BARGUEST HARBINGER OF DOOM

"And a dreadful thing from the cliff did spring;
Its wild bark thrilled around;
And a fiendish glow flashed forth I trow,
From the eyes of the Spectre Hound".
Traditional Ballad

WHILE nearly every town and hamlet along the Yorkshire coast boasts of its own particular ghost, there is one apparition common to all: the BARGUEST.

The Barguest has been described, BY THOSE WHO SURVIVED MEETING ONE as being like a huge, slathering black dog or demon, with eyes "as large as saucers" and "glowing like burning coals".

In towns, the dreadful howl of this animal is a sure harbinger of death, heard "by those whose time is nearly come". So strong was this belief along the coast, that it is said that a certain boy in Bridlington decided to terrify his aged granny by howling outside her window. Keen to see the effect, he went to peer through her letter box, hoping to find her shaking in fear. But what he saw left *him* shaking with fear. For when he peered in, he saw not his old granny, but the face of the dreaded Barguest peering back at him. The shock was so terrible that the little rogue sickened, fell ill and died within a week!

But Barguests spend most of their time out of town, waiting at GATES OR STILES for unfortunate travellers.

Some Barguests are simply mischievous, one, known as the "Picktree Brag" once allowed a farmer to ride as easily as if it was a placid mare, until it stopped suddenly in front of a pond, catapulting the surprised farmer into the stinking water and disappearing with a mocking howl. Others, however, are not so pleasant, and many were known to kill and eat unsuspecting travellers.

The most recent sightings of a Barguest occurred to the north of Whitby, on the Kettleness Cliffs. In the spring of 1974, rumours of a terrible black beast began to spread, and the locals became so terrified that an exorcist was called in. This priest, aptly named Daved Omen, carried out a service to rid the area of the Barguest, and wrote in a book about his experiences. As he prayed, the Barguest appeared, first as a vague mist, but growing larger and more solid in form with every passing second. His helpers fled in terror dropping their holy water as they ran, leaving poor Daved to his fate. But just before the animal grew big enough and solid enough to eat him, he cried out "Begone in the name of the Lord Jesus Christ. Begone to the place appointed for you, there to remain for ever. Be gone in the name of Christ", and the apparition disappeared, never to be seen again along the Kettleness cliffs.

Which is very good news if you are a walker travelling the "CLEVELAND WAY" along the cliffs from Whitby to Staithes. You are safe: you will not meet the Barguest. On the other hand, should you be going the other way, following the route down to Robin Hood's Bay, then we can give no guarantee that a hungry Barguest is not waiting for you at some isolated gate or stile along the way!

THE GHOSTS OF SKIPSEA CASTLE

THERE stands at Skipsea a few dreary remains of the castle of DROGO DE BEVERE, one of William the Conqueror's favourite knights.

Drogo fought bravely at the Battle of Hastings, but endeared himself to William mostly by his actions at the king's coronation in Westminster Abbey. When the crown was placed on William's head, a rousing traditional song was begun, in Anglo-Saxon. Drogo, speaking only French, and not understanding it, suspected some plot was afoot to kill the king and BEHEADED several choir boys before he could be calmed down. William rewarded Drogo for his actions by presenting him his niece for marriage, and giving him the huge estate of Holderness and a fine castle at Skipsea.

It is said that Drogo, growing impatient with his young wife, who refused on any account to eat sea food, eventually disposed of her by POISON. Some say he gave it to her by pretending it was a love potion, and others that he poisoned her by accident, serving her up the same piece of LOBSTER which she had refused day after day until, desperate with hunger, she had eaten the rotting flesh and died. Whatever the truth, Drogo was quick-witted enough to rush and visit the king before news of his niece's death could reach him, borrow a large sum of money, and flee the country, never to return.

Drogo's wife, LADY DE BEVERE, still haunts the remains of the castle. Her ghastly white figure is occasionally seen in moonlight, beckoning to passers-by, hoping that they will follow to the spot where her bones lie in a shallow, hasty grave and give them a proper Christian burial. **SADLY**, the passers-by, when confronted by the sight of a waving, luminous ghost beckoning, tend to go in the opposite direction to that desired by poor Lady De Bevere.

BUT IT IS NOT HER GHOST which the people of Skipsea chiefly fear. There are four holes close together in the castle's moat, each the size of a man's foot. Tradition has it that during the English Civil War, two brothers, arguing about their inheritance fought here. As they battled it out with swords and daggers, swearing and cursing at one another, their feet sank into the soft ground, preventing either from escaping. so that both were mortally wounded. To this day the sound of their fighting, and their dreadful oaths can be heard on still nights. It is said that anyone who comes across this scene and sees the two battling figures, will find soon after that his family is split by feuds or tragedy.

MERMAIDS *AND* MERMEN

MERMAIDS may seem mythical creatures to us today, but were often seen and even captured in times past. The Royal Navy certainly took them seriously enough, and kept records of sightings well into the nineteenth century.

Both **STAITHES AND SKINNINGROVE** at one time or other boasted captive "Merpersons", though their treatment of them was rather different. A sixteenth century account of the Merman of Skinningrove, written only thirty years after the events, gives full details of his time in the village. He was caught in nets just off the coast then locked in a house near the water's edge. The locals treated him quite **HOSPITABLY**, though they kept him imprisoned. They fed him with a variety of foods, but soon discovered he liked only **RAW FISH** and with this they supplied him copiously everyday. The ladies of the village visited him frequently, as he proved very partial to **FEMALE** company. He was regarded as having human intelligence, but was unable to communicate because his voice was limited to making "**SKREAKING**" noises. Gradually, as his gentle demeanour won over the people, he was given greater freedom, and allowed out of the house under guard. Eventually, since he showed no sign of trying to escape, he was given the freedom to roam the village, whereupon, he shuffled off into the sea. He disappeared forever beneath the waves, but not before he glanced back at his hosts with a look which to those observing it suggested a mixture of sorrow at leaving and gratitude for the good treatment he had received.

How different was the treatment meted out to the two mermaids captured in **STAITHES**! They were **IMPRISONED** in an old shed, fed only ROTTEN FISH GUTS and exhibited for a few pennies as curiosities to the townsfolk. The shed they were locked in was dark and dirty, and soon the mermaids became depressed and ill. However, one evening, they succeeded in forcing open the door of their prison and slipped into the water before they could be stopped. Out to sea, one of the two rose out of the water on her tail and shouted back a curse:

"BY THE CHIMES OF HILDA'S BELL,
THE SEA SHALL FLOW TO JACKDAW WELL".*

This well or spring was, at that time, someway inland. But a few months later, a great storm came and washed away thirteen houses and a large spit of land between the well and the sea, fulfilling the mermaid's VENGEFUL PROPHESY.

* The bells of St Hilda's Abbey, according to legend, lie under the sea at Black Nab near Whitby, and are said to ring on Halloween. The Story of these bells can be found in "13 Ghost Stories From Whitby" also published by Cædmon Storytellers.

Page 31

ST JOHN *OF* BRIDLINGTON
AND OTHER "BOLLINGTON" GHOSTS

ST. JOHN OF BRIDLINGTON was born in the little village of Thwing 9 miles from the town. He entered the Priory of Bridlington as a young man, and worked his way to the top. He was famously pious, and good to the poor. In 1401, after his death, he was made a saint. Many people visited his shrine, and many miracles are supposed to have happened there. One of the better known ones comes from the fifteenth century, when a ship coming down the coast from HARTLEPOOL was caught in a dreadful storm off the town. The waves were so big that the crew, expecting every second to be drowned, threw themselves down and prayed for salvation. At that point a particularly large wave lifted their vessel so high that even on their knees they were able to see the Priory Church of St. John in the old town. Taking this as a sign, they promptly turned their supplications to that holy man, and were rewarded a few seconds later when the ghost of St. John, dressed in his best bishops robes, was seen swimming through the seething waters towards them. The worthy saint, taking a rope from the front of the boat in his teeth, swam back to shore, pulling the boat safely into the harbour.

In more recent times, (1987), a less helpful ghost than that of St. John took up residence on a local trawler, called the Pickering. Immediately things began to go wrong, the radar broke down, lights mysteriously flickered on and off, while strange footsteps could be heard echoing through the boat. So dogged was the vessel with bad luck that within a few few months the captain could not persuade his crew onboard, the men preferring to "sign on the dole" rather than risk going to sea with the "flat capped" ghost which, they said, haunted the deck at night. The local labour exchange decided that their cheapest course of action was to employ a vicar to go to sea with the vessel and there bless it. This was done, successfully. No more was ever seen or heard of the ghost. The crew **CHEERFULLY** left the warmth and comfort of their homes, and to this day toil upon the pitching deck of their vessel, lashed by rain and storm, muttering grateful thanks to the priest!

THE TOWN ITSELF suffered a plague of ghosts in 1996, hardly a week passing without new tales emerging of ghostly goings on.

In January, Jane Malpass became a victim *"I felt there was somebody else in the room with me. At first I thought I was imagining things but then things started moving"* she told the Scarborough Evening News. Despite calling in the local vicar to exorcise the spirit, Jane and her daughter were forced out of their flat, sick and tired of the ghost throwing the child's toys about.

In March of the year same year, the canon of the Priory Church was called in to the house of Barry and Becky Robinson to rid them of a spirit which threw furniture around and put the kettle on every time their baby cried! He too failed, and the Robinson's too were soon on the move.

Perhaps Jane Malpass and the Robinson's should have learned from the example of Mr and Mrs Hayes. When they discovered that their house was haunted by a ghost who was in the habit not only of scaring their cat, but popping his head through their bedroom door late at night and and singing, they chose to adopted him, and get on his good side. And their kind attitude has been rewarded.

"We have all become quite fond of him over the years", says Mrs Hayes, "he seems to arrive when there is some kind of upset in the family, or when one of us is worried about something. It is almost like he is telling us not to panic, because he is looking after us and everything will be okay. It is actually very comforting to have him around."

THE OYSTER MAN
OF WHITBY

TODAY we think of OYSTERS as a rich man's food, eaten in exclusive restaurants with a glass of Champagne. How different it was two hundred years ago when "The Oyster Man" was a familiar figure in most towns, plying his wares round the public houses. At that time, oysters were a working man's food, downed with plenty of beer and brown bread: the pork scratchings of their day.

GADGY CLARKE was the Oyster Man of Whitby, making his daily round of the town's pubs, crying as he went "Oysters alive-oh!" in his weak, reedy voice. He was a small, thin man, whose long skinny neck seemed barely able to support the large oyster basket which he carried on his head.

In contrast to Gadgy was JONATHAN SMITH, a big, dark, muscular man; a violent fellow, whose piercing eyes no man dared meet. How he made his living no one knew. He would disappear for weeks or months at a time, returning in the dead of night. Some said he was a smuggler, others a highway man, some even that he was a fabulously rich Lord who had sold his soul to the devil. However he came by his money, it was sufficient to allow him to live extravagantly and keep several thorough bred horses, which he rode madly round the countryside, his head tilted back, his famous (and feared) howls of laughter cannoning off the trees and hedges.

It was on a cold and blustery NOVEMBER night as Jonathan Smith was drinking in the bar of the GOLDEN LION, that he heard old Gadgy's call. "Come in, come in!" he shouted, rapping on the window. A few seconds later the Oyster Man entered the room. Now, Jonathan Smith always had around him a group of **TOADIES**, loungers and ne-er do wells, whom he lorded over. Much to their delight Smith immediately began to insult Gadgy and his oysters. Gadgy was a little annoyed by this. He muttered a quiet oath and turned to go. But his words were not so quiet as to go unnoticed by some of the loungers in the bar. Smith was enraged: he could not bear to be insulted in front of his "friends". He snatched Gadgy's basket and threw it into the fire, then with his massive hand grabbed the oyster man himself and threatened to do the same to him. Gadgy, timid though he was, did what he could to protect himself, and stabbed the bully with the small knife he used to open the oysters' shells. To everyone's surprise, Smith, a mortal wound to his heart, fell dead on the spot.

In court Gadgy was found **NOT GUILTY** of murder and was released. But despite the Judge and Jury, Gadgy never appeared to forgive **HIMSELF** for the death of Jonathan Smith. He continued his rounds, his head sunk low with remorse, tears often dripping from his nose. But his cry of "**OYSTERS ALIVE - OH!**" was never more heard near the Golden Lion, for he took a circuitous route to avoid it, and within a year, weighed down with guilt, he died.

On stormy nights Gadgy's ghost still flits from pub to pub, his reedy voice heard faintly in the wind: "Oysters alive-oh!" However, in death, as in life, Gadgy shuns the Golden Lion, providing a refuge from his ghost for the more apprehensive drinker.

Whether Smith lies easy in his grave, is of course another matter. No guarantee can be given that his spirit will not come visiting the site of his death: his fearsome black, piercing eyes appearing before the timid, ghost-avoiding customer with a **WILD AND SAVAGE HOWL OF LAUGHTER.**

THE RED ROCK
OF SALTWICK

IN MEDIAEVAL TIMES, being the eldest son of a wealthy father was a good thing to be, for all the family wealth, lands, treasure and titles would, in time, fall to you. In expectation of your coming good fortune, your father's friends would encourage their prettiest daughter to be nice to you, hoping that you would marry her.

How different was the fate of a younger brother! The best he could hope was that his father might make some small provision for him, either paying for him to become a priest, so living out a lonely bachelor life in some rural parish, or giving him a small piece of land to farm as a lowly yeoman. In church he would find the ugly, squint eyed daughter of his neighbour simpering at him, knowing that she too must make do with second best. He was doomed to be ever the "poor relation", occasionally invited to the manor house for a meal with his fat, buck-toothed wife, seeing his brother enjoy a life much richer than his simply because he had the fortune to be born first.

Two such brothers were Stephen and Gervase. Gervase was the eldest, a knight of the shire, and married to one of the most beautiful woman in England. Stephen was the younger. He had received a small settlement from his father, and through hard work had increased his wealth until he could become a knight, though he struggled hard to maintain the expense of his horse and armour.

Stephen was an unhappy man on two counts. Firstly he resented his brother's good fortune in being the first born, and believed that had their roles been reversed, then Gervase would never have been able improve himself in the way he had done. Secondly, and more importantly: he was deeply in love with his brother's wife.

Gervase, with his inherited privilege, was in his own way unhappy. Aware that he had not earned his wealth, he felt unworthy, and so dedicated himself to religion, hoping in some way that this would atone for his unmerited fortunes.

On one occasion, Stephen, knowing his brother was away on pilgrimage to the shrine of St Hilda at Whitby, went to see his sister in law, determined to let her know how he felt about her, and try to persuade her to run away with him. She was horrified when he revealed his heart to her, and sent him away, threatening that she would tell all to her husband if he ever came near her again.

Stephen was devastated. For a time he sat with a knife beside him, thinking of suicide. Then another, darker thought came into his head: if he were to kill Gervase, all his troubles would be resolved. He would inherit his brother's lands, and would soon, he thought, win round the widow.

With this evil plan in mind, he leapt upon his horse and made off for Whitby. Finding a spot ideally suited for an ambush on the beach at Saltwick where his brother must certainly pass on his way home, he waited. For two days Stephen lurked in a cave, neither eating or drinking. The tide washed into the hiding place, almost drowning him, but cold and dirty as he was he waited still. Finally, he was rewarded when he saw the figure of his brother approach, riding some way ahead of his servants.

Stephen leaped from his hiding place, and stabbed his brother through the heart. Gervase fell from his horse onto a large, flat rock, which in seconds became soaked with his blood. Gervase looked up and recognised Stephen. With his dying breath he shouted "FALSE BROTHER, FLEE FAR AS THOU WILT, THIS BLOOD-STAINED STONE SHALL BE THY DEATH-BED!"

The servants had seen everything from a distance. They rushed to their master, but were too late: by then Gervase had died and "the mad hermit", as they described the scruffy assailant, had escaped.

Stephen now inherited his brother's estate, and was lord of an extensive manor. Gervase's widow, on Stephen's invitation, stayed on in the castle, lulled from any suspicion of his motives by his gentle treatment and consideration towards her. But soon he began to apply pressure on her to marry him. First with tales of duty and promises of love, and later by threats and curses. Finally, enraged, Stephen locked her in a cellar before getting very drunk. The following day he got drunk again, and fell into a stupor which lasted two days. At the end of this time, he remembered his sister in law, and went to visit her in the cold dungeon, hoping to prevail on her. But too late. During his drunken binge, the poor woman had died of cold and thirst.

Stephen fell into despair, and for over a year constantly drank to keep from thinking of the foul double murder which he had committed. Eventually the drink could not save him from his sorrows. He sobered up, and decided that he must atone for his sins. He became a tireless worker for the poor, and had a chapel built at Kilburn just north of London in honour of his brother. The altar of this chapel he had made from slabs of rock brought specially from Saltwick, the spot where his brother died. Amazingly, one of these stones was the very one on which his brother had fallen, still stained with his blood. Stephen saw this as a sign, and redoubling his good works, had a hospital for the poor built by the side of the chapel.

After 40 years of good works, Stephen, falling ill, and knowing that he did not have long to live, made his way to the chapel and confessed his sins to the priest. As penance he had to pray for forgiveness of his sins by his brother's tomb. As he knelt in prayer, gazing at the red stain on the alter, his brother's dying words came back to him again - "FALSE BROTHER, FLEE FAR AS THOU WILT, THIS BLOOD-STAINED STONE SHALL BE THY DEATH-BED!"

The following morning, the priest entered the church and found Steven lying on the red-stained stone, cold and dead.

The story of Gervase and Steven became well known, and a ballad was composed about the brothers, as a warning against the sin of covetousness. Here are the words.

By the blessed rood for Gervase the good the nuns of Kilburn pray;
But for the wretch who shed his blood, Not one a prayer shall say.

The bells shall ring and the saints shall sing Sir Gervase to the blest;
But holiest rites can never bring the murderer's soul to rest.

Now tell me, I pray, thou palmer gray who kneelest at this shrine,
Why dost thou cry so eagerly for the help that is Divine?

That stone was then on Whitby shore, and now behold it here;
The blood runs wet, I see it yet, and still the voice I hear."

False brother, upon thy flying steed, thou canst not flee so fast,
But on this stone, where now I bleed, thyself shall breathe thy last.

The sun in the west sinks red to his rest, his light is red on thy face;
And an awful sign in that deep red shrine, like a dead man's blood I trace.

Oh speak not thus, thou holy man, but kneel and pray for me;
I've groaned and wept, and vigils kept, and wandered o'er land and sea.

With book and with bede, with Ave and creed, oh help me while you may;
When the clock strikes one. then leave me alone. for alone
I then must pray."

With the morning light the good monk came, by the sorrowful man to pray;
But the life was flown, and on that stone, a corse the palmer lay.

PENNEL'S POOL, HORNSEA

MAKING A LIVING from fishing has always been a precarious occupation, and so it is not surprising to discover that the fishermen of Yorkshire often put their vessels to other uses. Today the occasional boat is used to take visitors out to sea for pleasure trips, but in the past they were more likely to turn their hands to SMUGGLING. During the Napoleonic wars, smuggling, or "the free trade" as they preferred to call it, was an important, even vital part of the economy. The fishing boats would sail out to meet a foreign boat at some prearranged rendezvous, load up with contraband - brandy, lace or tea - and land it at some secluded spot, before taking it inland to sell at a HANDSOME PROFIT.

But smuggling had its own problems: if a smuggler was robbed or swindled, he found that since his activities were illegal he could not turn to the authorities for help. Instead, he found, a new law applied, the LAW OF THE JUNGLE. By this law, the strong prey upon the weak. A smuggler soon discovered that while a moonless night was good for smuggling, it was also ideal for ambushes; for treachery; for knives slipped unexpectedly into the back.

In the GODLESS AND LAWLESS TOWN OF FILEY, there once lived Abraham Pennel, a fearless and desperate man; a smuggler; pirate and robber. His boat, a well armed cutter, was manned by a crew almost as desperate as himself, and was the TERROR OF THE EAST COAST.

Pennel was particularly successful at intercepting and robbing other smugglers, for he had a network of spies:

drunkards and loafers who sat in pubs up and down the coast. These rapscallions passed on to him any whispers and rumours of smuggling which they overheard.

The group who suffered most from the activities of Pennel were the FISHERMEN OF HORNSEA, for the people of that town were once renowned along the coast as gossips, whom it was said could not keep a secret even if their very lives depended on it.

It is interesting to note that the people of Hornsea were equally noted for their superstitious nature. They attributed Pennel's success not to their gossiping, (for none of them thought they were gossips) but to the terrifying supernatural powers which they imagined he had; they were very much afraid of him.

Four of the bravest men in the village, however, made plans to MURDER PENNEL, and thereby end his reign of terror. They sailed up to Bridlington, then walked along the coast To Filey, slipping down the hill at sunset to the alehouse where they knew Pennel would be supping.

Perhaps Pennel noticed them peering in through the window, or may be (as was afterwards said) one of them had been "gossiping like an old woman", for when they entered the tavern, he was ready for them. Swinging round from the bar he pulled out a pistol and brandished it, shouting: "THE FIRST MAN TO RAISE HIS ARM COMES WITH ME TO HELL!"

The fishermen stood still, as if turned to stone, for though Pennel's pistol had only one shot in it, and they themselves were armed, they dared not make a move, for none of them cared to take accompany Pennel on that particular journey! Slowly, eyes blazing, Pennel walked towards the fishermen, who parted to let him pass. He turned and inched backwards to the door then slipped out. For a second the fishermen stood still, then as if a spell had been broken, they rushed in pursuit. Pennel, some twenty yards down the road, turned and fired his weapon, causing the fishermen to throw themselves to the ground. By the time they regained their feet, Pennel was nowhere to be seen. And now it was they who were in danger, for this was Pennel's town, and who could tell what might be waiting around the next corner for them. The fishermen wisely beat a retreat, running back up the hill and away. A few of the local children were even bold enough to greet them in the traditional Filey manner, jeering and throwing stones at them.

But Pennel's brave actions were to be his undoing. The tale was soon well known up and down the coast, and the four fishermen of Hornsea, humiliated and stung by being labeled both gossips and cowards, came up with a second plan. They let it be known around the local alehouses that they had a store of smuggled goods, and that on a certain night they were to take these along a quiet lane to meet a rascally old parson who had agreed to buy the lot. This news soon reached Pennel. On the night, confident that he could deal with the fishermen, left his gang behind. Sure enough the four fishermen ran away as soon as Pennel appeared, leaving behind their horse well laden with barrels of brandy and boxes of tea. Pennel continued along the lane, leading the horse, for it was his plan was to rob the parson who was coming to buy the goods too! Pennel chuckled as he went along until he came upon the AMBUSH SET BY THE REVENUE MEN, whom the four fishermen had also thoughtfully told about the smuggled goods. After a short but vicious fight, Pennel was arrested and thrown into York Gaol.

With Pennel was out of the way, many people who he had harmed gained the courage to inform against him, and several cases of murder and piracy were brought against him. He was tried, found guilty, and condemned to death.

It was decided that Pennel should be executed at the coast which he had terrorised, and his body left, bound in iron hoops as a warning to other pirates. And so it was in February 1770, that he was taken in a cart from York to Hornsea to be hanged on a gallows built by the cliff's edge just north of the town.

While most criminals are a little subdued on their way to the gallows, Pennel stayed true to his character, fighting with his gaolers, shaking his fist and cursing the fishermen who lined the road through Hornsea to watch his final journey. When the rope was put around his neck, Pennel signaled to the priest who was present. The priest, thinking that Pennel wanted to make a final confession, or to pray, drew near. Pennel began to whisper a few words, and when the priest leaned closer still, he lurched forwards and bit off this good man's ear.

The cart was driven forwards and Pennel launched into eternity, a curse and the priest's ear still upon his lips.

Even after he was dead, Pennel continued to blight the lives of the superstitious folk of Hornsea. Fearing that he had put a curse on them, they would not go near the spot where he was hanged and would walk half a mile inland to avoid the sight of Pennel's corpse swinging too and fro in the breeze.

In 1810, the muddy cliff on which the gallows stood collapsed in a winter storm, and Pennel's skeleton disappeared into the sea. But this was no relief for the superstitious people of Hornsea, however: the fishermen were now forced to take a huge detour, a mile to the south to avoid "Pennel's Pool" a stretch of water to the north of the town. For they believed that this water was haunted by **PENNEL'S VENGEFUL SPIRIT**, his hands lurking just below surface to drag the unwary out of their boats and down into the depths to his sharpened, waiting teeth!

BETWEEN THE HUMBER
AND THE TEES

THE YORKSHIRE COAST begins and ends with two great rivers, the Humber and the Tees. Both of these rivers run into the sea by a featureless, marshy coastline, and strangely have similar legends associated with them.

THE HUMBER ends at Spurn Point, a shifting spit of barren sand that sticks forlornly out into the North Sea. The coast here is subject to erosion, and there are many old tales of **VILLAGES WASHED AWAY**, whose church bells still toll beneath the waters, of **PHANTOM ROMAN ARMIES** marching far out to sea along long vanished roads. The formost of these tales, however, concerns Ravenspurg, a fine city that stood on the Humber banks a mile or so from the river's mouth.

Ravenspurg was founded by an enterprising trader who sold food and drink from a wrecked boat on the shore to mariners who were anchored in the Humber's mouth waiting for favourable wind or tide. The City quickly grew, and obtained a royal charter for a weekly market and an annual six day fair. It was once was so rich and successful that it sent two MPs to parliament, and the Burghers of Hull sent a petition to the king complaining that its wealthy neighbour was damaging its trade.

It is said that one day a **HUNGRY BEGGAR** came to Ravenspurg, but was turned away empty handed from every single door. Some people even chased him, throwing stones at his head. **DISGUSTED**, the beggar left the city, but looking back, he laid a curse on it, so that the waters of the Humber rose, and Ravensurg disappeared beneath the flowing current, never to be seen again.

Whether there is any truth to the legend we cannot say, but of Ravenspurg there is nothing left but the market cross which stands almost forgotten in the churchyard of the little village of Howden a few miles up the river from the "DROWNED CITY".

The Tees flows into the sea just north of Redcar, and should have been the site of a great port, for plans were made in the early nineteenth century to build a huge harbour on the rocky scaur which runs out to sea, providing a much needed haven for sailing ships traveling along the dangerous Yorkshire coast. However, before a single brick was laid, steam began to take the place of sail, and the plan was abandoned.

Beyond the steel works, on the southern bank of the Tees, close to "PADDY'S ISLAND", and buried beneath millions of tons of steel "slag", lie the remains of a fort; the last refuge of the Anglo-Saxons who refused to accept William the Conqueror as their king. In 1072 the villagers of "SAINT SULPICUS", just down the coast betrayed them to the King who led an army from York to attack them. The refugees managed to escape, but the fort was abandoned.

King William rewarded the villagers of Saint Sulpicus by giving them his war helmet, stuffed with gold coins. However, before these treacherous wretches could share out their ill-gotten gains, their village was destroyed by divine wrath, a huge storm washing the village, and villagers, into the sea. On one night of the year, the souls of these villagers are said to appear on the beach BEWAILING their fate, and desperately searching for their lost gold.

They that go down to the sea in ships, that do
business in great waters; These see the works of
the LORD, and his wonders in the deep.
psalm 107 vs 23&24

THE END

ALSO BY THE CAEDMON STORYTELLERS

THE WITCHES OF NORTH YORKSHIRE A chance to meet the notorious witches of North Yorkshire. All of these women actually lived, but whether they could really cast spells or fly about on broomsticks we cannot say. What is important though, is that their **NEIGHBOURS BELIEVED THEY COULD,** and the tales of their antics, passed down through the generations are still with us today.

THIRTEEN GHOST STORIES FROM WHITBY Caedmon Storyteller's first and most popular book. In these pages you will find Whitby Ghost Stories, old and new. Some can be heard **WHISPERED** in dark corners of the town's ancient inns..... Some no one dare speak of at all!

Available from local bookshops and online
https://whitbyhairbraids.etsy.com